Welcome to
Computers for
ESL Students:
Workbook

OLIVIA ADENDORFF
Manteca Adult School

LOIS WOODEN
Manteca Adult School

LABYRINTH
PUBLICATIONS®

El Sobrante, CA

D1366889

President:
Brian Favro

COO:
Ted Ricks

Series Editor:
Russel Stolins

Managing Editor:
Laura A. Lionello

Production Manager:
Rad Proctor

Editorial/Production Team:
Amy Berk, Document Jones

Indexing:
Afterwords Editorial Services

Cover Design:
Huckdesign

LABYRINTH
PUBLICATIONS®
El Sobrante, CA

Welcome to Computers for ESL Students: Workbook
by Olivia Adendorff and Lois Wooden

Copyright © 2006 by Labyrinth Publications

Labyrinth Publications
P.O. Box 20820
El Sobrante, California 94803
800.522.9746
On the Web at labpub.com

ISBN-13:   978-1-59136-107-7
ISBN-10:   1-59136-107-9

Manufactured in the United States of America.

07 08 09   0 9 8 7 6 5 4

Table of Contents

Learning About Computer Basics

WORKBOOK 1.1 Fill in the Blanks

Write the name of each item that the arrow is pointing to.

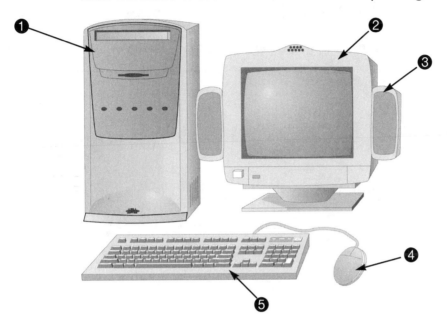

1. _____

2. _____

3. _____

4. _____

5. _____

Paired Conversation

With a partner, take turns reading the A and B parts of the conversation. Fill in each blank with the right word (or words) from the Word Bank.

WORD BANK

computer	exciting	CPU	brain	monitor
screen	keyboard	keyboarding	mouse	buttons
push	turn on	power button	Desktop	computer

Student A	Hi. What's that?
Student B	This is my new _____.
Student A	Really? How _____!
Student B	Let me show you. This is the _____.
Student A	I know. It's the _____.
Student B	That's right! This is the _____.
Student A	Wow! It has a nice _____.
Student B	I know. This is called the _____.
Student A	Yeah, I know that word. My brother takes _____ at school.
Student B	This is the _____ and these are the mouse _____.
Student A	What a cute mouse. Can I _____ the button?
Student B	Not yet! You have to _____ the computer first.
Student A	OK. Can I push the _____ to turn it on now?
Student B	Sure.
Student A	The first thing you see is the _____.
Student B	The colors look good.
Student A	I know. I love my new _____!
Student B	You are so lucky!

Vocabulary Worksheet

Fill in the blanks. Select the best answer for each sentence, using your vocabulary words from the Word Bank.

WORD BANK

CPU	Desktop	icon
keyboard	monitor	mouse
mouse button	power button	screen

1. To turn on the computer, press the _____.

2. You type on the _____. It has letters, symbols, and functions.

3. An _____ is a picture that represents a program or command.

4. A _____ is the part of the computer system that includes the screen and its controls.

5. The _____ is the part of the computer that lights up and shows what is happening on the computer.

6. The _____ is the first thing you see on your screen when you turn on your computer.

7. When you use the word "click," it means that you press the _____.

8. The _____ lets you point to different things on the computer screen.

9. The _____ is where all the "thinking" is done.

Fill in the blanks. Select the best answer for each sentence, using vocabulary words from the Word Bank.

WORD BANK

turn on	turn off	go to
press	let go	tap
click	drag	select

1. To press and let go of the mouse button in one smooth motion is to

   _____.

2. Before you can use a computer, you must _____ the CPU and

   the monitor.

3. To quickly and softly press down a button to get a response is called to

   _____.

4. To _____ means to take your finger off the mouse button

   after you press it.

5. When you choose something in particular, you _____ it.

6. To turn on your computer, you have to _____ the power button.

7. When you are finished using the computer, you should _____

   the computer.

8. When you want to move something to a different position, you can

   _____ it with your mouse.

9. To _____ means to take your mouse pointer to a place on

   your screen.

Missing Vowels and Consonants

Fill in the missing vowels of the nouns in the left column and the missing consonants of the verbs in the right column. Remember: some are multiword terms.

1. Dsktp _____

2. ms _____

3. cn _____

4. CP _____

5. pwr bttn _____

6. ms bttn _____

7. lt g _____

8. kybrd _____

9. mntr _____

10. trn n _____

11. clck _____

12. tp _____

13. g t _____

14. drg _____

15. slct _____

16. scrn _____

17. prss _____

18. trn ff _____

Scrambled Words

Unscramble the letters to create words from the vocabulary list. Remember: some are multiword terms.

1. CUP _____

2. tueboonrpwt _____

3. rotmino _____

4. nersec _____

5. daobkyre _____

6. eusom _____

7. mosebtnuotu _____

8. sekotdp _____

9. noic _____

10. runton _____

11. rffunto _____

12. pesrs _____

13. cklic _____

14. gotel _____

15. ogot _____

16. letces _____

17. pat _____

18. darg _____

Word Search

Find the words listed in the Word Bank. Spaces and hyphens do not appear in the puzzle.

WORD BANK

CLICK	CPU	DESKTOP	DRAG	GO TO	ICON
KEYBOARD	LET GO	MONITOR	MOUSE	MOUSE BUTTON	POWER BUTTON
PRESS	SCREEN	SELECT	TAP	TURN OFF	TURN ON

```
M  O  U  S  E  B  U  T  T  O  N  N  R  D  N
M  K  V  K  I  J  Y  I  H  V  O  X  E  U  O
F  J  E  L  Q  J  V  P  V  T  W  S  I  F  N
C  G  Y  Y  N  O  C  I  T  U  K  I  D  D  R
I  H  A  I  B  T  R  U  P  T  A  P  W  P  U
Z  Y  O  J  C  O  B  C  O  M  H  F  H  S  T
B  P  F  E  B  R  A  P  X  O  X  B  L  I  D
G  M  L  J  E  R  V  R  J  N  I  A  E  U  L
Q  E  U  W  K  W  B  T  D  I  M  O  U  S  E
S  N  O  F  F  O  N  R  U  T  A  O  C  T  T
G  P  E  O  F  G  P  L  P  O  B  L  T  U  G
A  G  Z  E  U  U  F  R  T  R  I  V  Y  O  O
R  H  A  T  R  G  E  B  E  C  T  C  I  V  G
D  C  N  E  G  C  Y  S  K  S  R  Z  N  V  U
E  K  B  T  R  B  S  T  Y  M  S  S  Q  E  L
```

Fill in the words down and across to complete the puzzle.

ACROSS

4. To take your finger off the mouse button

5. To take your mouse pointer to a place on your screen

7. To push a button with your finger

10. To give power to the computer

11. The first thing that you see on your screen when you turn the computer on

13. The part of the monitor that lights up and shows what is happening on the computer

15. A picture that represents a program or command

16. Brain of the computer system

DOWN

1. The part that you type on that has all the letters, symbols, and functions

2. The button that turns the computer on

3. To go to a particular thing and use your mouse to take it to a different position

6. The part of the computer that you look at to see your work

8. To choose a program, paragraph, or icon

9. The small oval piece that you can use to move from one part of the screen to another

10. To quickly and softly press a button to get a response

12. To stop the power from going to the computer

14. To press and let go of the mouse button

Using Windows and the Start Menu

WORKBOOK 2.1 Fill in the Blanks

Write the correct word to describe each part of the Windows Desktop.

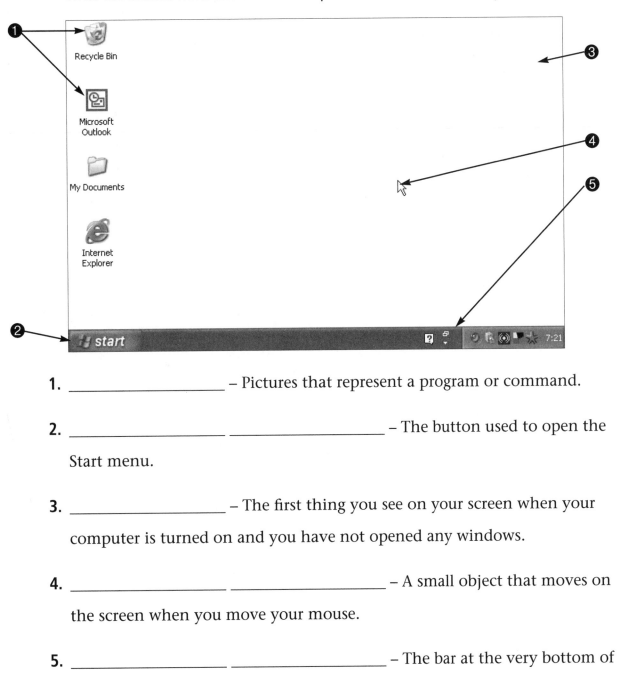

1. _____ – Pictures that represent a program or command.

2. _____ _____ – The button used to open the Start menu.

3. _____ – The first thing you see on your screen when your computer is turned on and you have not opened any windows.

4. _____ _____ – A small object that moves on the screen when you move your mouse.

5. _____ _____ – The bar at the very bottom of the screen. It shows all programs that are open.

WORKBOOK 2.2 **Fill in the Blanks**

Write the name of each item that the arrow is pointing to.

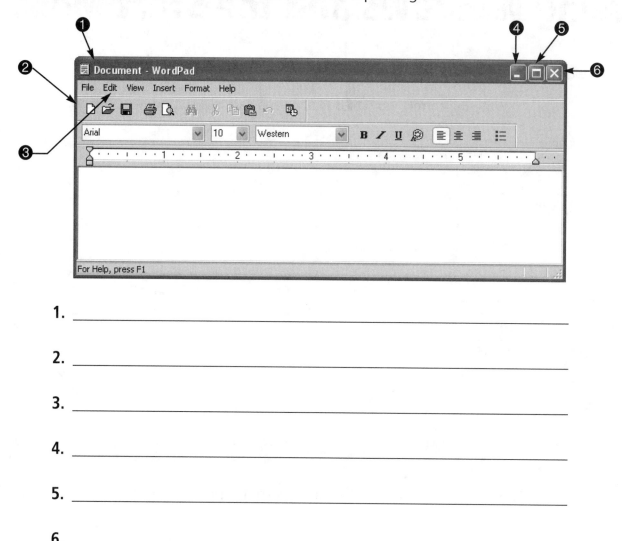

1. _____

2. _____

3. _____

4. _____

5. _____

6. _____

WORKBOOK 2.3 Paired Conversation

With a partner, take turns reading the A and B parts of the conversation. Fill in each blank with the right word (or words) from the Word Bank.

WORD BANK

close	open	screen	computer	window
Start button	Start menu	title bar	menu bar	toolbar

Student A	Good morning.
Student B	Hi. What are we studying today?
Student A	I think we are going to learn how to open and _____ a window.
Student B	Do you mean if the temperature gets too hot in here?
Student A	No! I mean to _____ a window on our computers.
Student B	My computer doesn't have any windows. It only has a _____.
Student A	Don't be silly! There are windows inside your _____.
Student B	Oh! How do you open a _____?
Student A	Well, we will learn that today.
Student B	Will we have to use the _____?
Student A	Yes, and the _____ too.
Student B	That will be interesting.
Student A	We'll learn about different parts of a window.
Student B	I know about the _____.
Student A	That's great. You'll learn about the _____ too.
Student B	What else is important to learn?
Student A	Well, the _____ tells you what tools you can use.
Student B	I can't wait to start!

Fill in the blanks. Select the best answer for each sentence, using vocabulary words from the Word Bank.

WORD BANK

window	Close button	title bar
Minimize button	Maximize button	Start button
Start menu	Restore button	task bar
menu bar	program	toolbar

1. The square button between Minimize and Close that makes your window fill the whole screen is called the _____.

2. The button that opens the Start menu and is on the bottom-left corner of your screen is the _____.

3. The bar at the bottom of the screen that shows all programs that are open is called the _____.

4. A rectangular area on the screen that shows a program or message is called a _____.

5. The _____ has different icons. Each icon does a different job when you click on it.

6. This button looks like a minus sign. It makes the window disappear, but the program is still open. It is called the _____.

7. The _____ shows when you click on the Start button. It lists the main programs.

8. The button with an X that closes the window is the _____. It makes the window disappear and closes the program.

9. The button in the same place as Maximize that changes a maximized window to a smaller size is the _____.

10. The _____ is below the title bar. It gives you choices for using the program.

11. The very top of a window that shows the name of the program you are using is called the _____.

12. A _____ is a set of directions that tells the computer what to do to get a job done.

Verb Worksheet

Fill in the blanks. Select the best answer for each sentence, using vocabulary words from the Word Bank.

WORD BANK

open	point	minimize
restore	maximize	close

1. To _____ means to make the window larger so it fills the entire screen.

2. To show a window, you have to _____ it.

3. To _____ means to change a maximized window to a smaller size.

4. To make the mouse pointer go over something that you want to choose is called to _____.

5. To keep a window open but make it disappear so that only its button shows on the task bar is to _____ it.

6. To stop a program so that it does not show on your screen is to _____ it.

WORKBOOK 2.6 Missing Vowels

Fill in the missing vowels to complete the nouns and verbs. Remember: some are multiword terms.

1. mnmz _____

2. pn _____

3. pnt _____

4. rstr _____

5. wndw _____

6. cls bttn _____

7. mxmz _____

8. cls _____

9. tlbr _____

10. mxmz bttn _____

11. mn br _____

12. mnmz bttn _____

13. rstr bttn _____

14. strt bttn _____

15. strt mn _____

16. tsk br _____

17. ttl br _____

Scrambled Words

Unscramble the letters to create computer vocabulary words. Remember: some are multiword terms.

1. soelc ttoubn _____

2. ratts eunm _____

3. unem arb _____

4. topin _____

5. treeors nutbot _____

6. ziiiemmn _____

7. askt arb _____

8. doinww _____

9. otol rab _____

10. exiimmaz nutbot _____

11. stereor _____

12. mmiiizen tuontb _____

13. poen _____

14. ratst ottunb _____

15. mmxzaiie _____

16. eiltt abr _____

17. sleoc _____

Word Search

Find the words listed in the Word Bank. Spaces and hyphens do not appear in the puzzle.

WORD BANK

CLOSE	CLOSE BUTTON	DISPLAY	MAXIMIZE	MAXIMIZE BUTTON
MENU	MINIMIZE	MINIMIZE BUTTON	OPEN	POINT
RESTORE	RESTORE BUTTON	START BUTTON	START MENU	TASK BAR
TITLE BAR	TOOLBAR	WINDOW		

```
R   W   S   G   R   S   S   V   W   P   X   M   N   M   T
A   V   Z   N   B   A   K   T   O   I   A   Z   I   E   I
B   W   F   O   G   P   B   I   A   X   N   N   Z   W   T
L   O   G   T   V   F   N   K   I   R   I   D   Y   F   L
O   C   O   T   L   T   E   M   S   M   T   A   O   N   E
O   L   D   U   I   N   I   O   I   A   L   M   O   W   B
T   O   N   B   B   Z   E   Z   B   P   T   T   E   F   A
M   S   Y   E   E   G   E   P   S   A   T   Y   Y   N   R
G   E   L   R   V   B   E   I   O   U   U   N   E   M   U
B   Q   O   O   U   F   D   Q   B   B   X   L   J   Z   E
X   N   O   T   T   U   B   E   Z   I   M   I   X   A   M
Q   K   T   S   I   H   S   E   Z   I   M   I   N   I   M
Z   O   F   E   V   O   R   E   S   T   O   R   E   G   B
N   P   G   R   L   T   H   O   L   D   N   Z   W   V   X
T   D   U   C   S   T   A   R   T   B   U   T   T   O   N
```

WORKBOOK 2.9 **Crossword Puzzle**

Fill in the words down and across to complete the puzzle.

ACROSS

1. A set of directions that tells the computer what to do to get a job done

3. To stop a program.

5. To show a window

7. To change a maximized window to a smaller size

8. The button that looks like a minus sign on the top-right of a window

11. A bar showing different icons that each do a different job

13. A rectangular area on the screen that shows a program or message

DOWN

2. The square button between Minimize and Close that makes a window fill the whole screen

3. The button with an X that closes the window

4. To make a window disappear (but not close) so that only its button shows on the taskbar

6. The bar with words on it that is below the title bar

8. To make the window larger so that it fills the entire screen

9. The bar at the top of a window that shows the name of the program you are using

10. The bar at the bottom of the screen that shows all open programs

12. To make the mouse pointer touch something that you want to choose

Using Windows Programs

WORKBOOK 3.1 Fill in the Blanks

Write the correct word that goes in each blank.

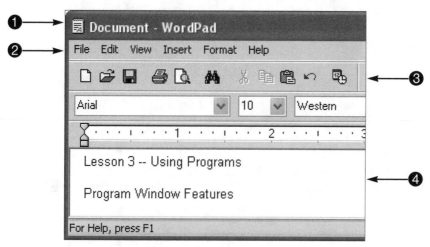

The WordPad Program Window

1. _____ _____ tells you what program you are using.

2. _____ _____ lists commands that let you do different things to your work.

3. _____ has icons that do different things when you click them.

4. _____ _____ is the place where your work shows when you put it in by typing or using the mouse.

Write the correct word that goes in each blank.

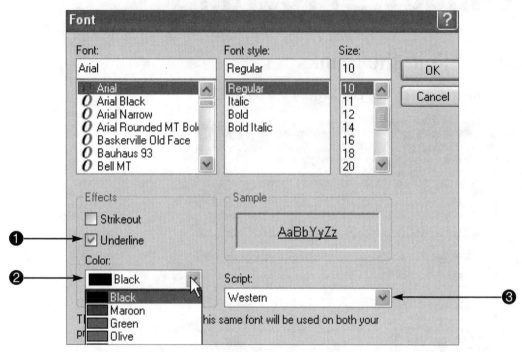

A WordPad Program Dialogue Box

1. You click in the _____ to check or uncheck them.

2. The _____ _____ _____

   _____ is a list of choices that opens when you click on it.

3. The _____ _____ _____

   _____ is the arrow you click on to open the drop-down

   list box.

Paired Conversation

With a partner, take turns reading the A and B parts of the conversation. Fill in each blank with the right word (or words) from the Word Bank.

WORD BANK

minimize	maximize	hardware	software
dialogue box	settings	computer game	play
check	clear		

Student A	Yesterday we learned how to _____ a window.
Student B	Yes, I remember. That was really good to learn.
Student A	Do you remember how to _____ a window?
Student B	Yes. Now, let's talk about what we learned today too.
Student A	Today we learned about _____.
Student B	Is that like the computer and the monitor?
Student A	Right. We also learned about _____.
Student B	That's like WordPad and the other things that are not hardware.
Student A	That's true.
Student B	We also learned about the _____.
Student A	Yes. Dialogue boxes are important.
Student B	What about _____?
Student A	Settings are really important. They decide so many things.
Student B	Did you play a _____ today?
Student A	Not really. I just watched somebody else _____.
Student B	We did practice how to _____ boxes.
Student A	Then we learned how to uncheck and _____ the boxes.
Student B	Well, I'm so glad that we remember so much!

Vocabulary Worksheet

Fill in the blanks. Select the best answer for each sentence, using vocabulary words from the Word Bank.

WORD BANK

drop-down list arrow	checkbox	hardware
drop-down list	dialogue box	software
settings	appearance	

1. _____ is the physical part of the computer system, like the monitor and the keyboard.

2. _____ is a box with a list that appears from top to bottom with more things you can do.

3. A window with boxes you can check to select what you want is called a _____.

4. A _____ is a box that you can check to choose something you want.

5. An arrow that you can click to make the drop-down list appear is called a _____.

6. _____ are information about how a program is set up.

7. Everything in the computer system that is not hardware is called _____.

8. The way something looks is called its _____.

Verb Worksheet

Fill in the blanks. Select the best answer for each sentence, using vocabulary words from the Word Bank.

WORD BANK

appear	check (a box)	clear
let up	play	preview
release	view	hold

1. You can _____ a document to see how it will look when you print it.

2. To _____ is to show on the screen so you can see it.

3. To uncheck a box is called to _____ it.

4. To _____ means to click the box so that a checkmark appears.

5. To look at something is to _____ it.

6. To _____ means to use a computer game.

7. To keep your finger pressed on the mouse button is to _____ the button.

8. To _____ means to take your finger off the mouse button.

9. To _____ means to release or let go of the button.

Missing Vowels and Consonants

Fill in the missing vowels of the nouns in the left column and the missing consonants of the verbs in the right column. Remember: some are multiword terms.

1. sttngs   _____

2. dlg bx   _____

3. chckbx   _____

4. pprnc   _____

5. drp dwn lst   _____

6. hrdwr   _____

7. prgrm   _____

8. sftwr   _____

9. drp dwn rrw _____

10. - i e -   _____

11. - - a -   _____

12. - - e - -   _____

13. - o - -   _____

14. - - e - i e -   _____

15. - - e a -   _____

16. - e - e a - e _____

17. - e -   u -   _____

18. a - - e a -   _____

Scrambled Words

Unscramble the letters to create your computer vocabulary words. Remember: some are multiword terms.

1. raetwsfo _____

2. daaewhrr _____

3. alpy _____

4. elt pu _____

5. orpd nwod warro _____

6. hecckxob _____

7. eeelars _____

8. ralec _____

9. prod wodn tisl _____

10. glueoida oxb _____

11. kecch _____

12. paarep _____

13. gintetss _____

14. ewiv _____

15. lohd _____

16. preeaaacnp _____

17. weepriv _____

18. grroamp _____

Word Search

Find the words listed in the Word Bank. Spaces and hyphens do not appear in the puzzle.

WORD BANK

APPEAR	APPEARANCE	CHECK	CHECKBOX
CLEAR	DIALOGUE BOX	DROP-DOWN ARROW	DROP-DOWN LIST
HARDWARE	HOLD	LET UP	PLAY
PREVIEW	PROGRAM	RELEASE	SETTINGS
SOFTWARE	VIEW		

```
E U S E M T E E L R D J D H P
W C I E V N R B E H R T W G R
H F N I T A I L L G O B Y X O
P A E A W T E W I Q P L D O G
R W T D R A I R S A D R K B R
M A R P S A E N M F O H C K A
X A E E L R E G G P W O E C M
H M S P A A C P D S N L H E S
B C T E P R Y O P V A D C H E
S N L J S A W A H A R H J C W
I C O Z Y N V X H Q R M U I L
J O I G L E T U P L O Z F G R
S Y R I B G S O F T W A R E Q
V W S X O B E U G O L A I D Z
I T R W E I V E R P E Z Q W G
```

Crossword Puzzle

Fill in the words down and across to complete the puzzle.

ACROSS

3. A list that appears from top to bottom with more things you can choose

7. To look at something

11. When something shows and you can see it

12. To click the box so that a checkmark appears

13. Information about how a program is set up

14. A box that you can check to choose something that you want

15. The physical part of the computer system

16. To use a computer game

DOWN

1. An arrow that you can click to make the drop-down list appear

2. To keep your finger pressed on the mouse button

4. To see how information will look when it prints

5. To release or let go of the mouse button

6. Everything in the computer system that is not hardware

8. The way something looks

9. A window with boxes you can check to select what you want

10. To take your finger off the mouse button

14. To click a button or box to remove what was there before

Creating a Document in WordPad

The Computer Keyboard

On each key in this picture of the keyboard, write the letter, number, or symbol from your computer keyboard. (Your keyboard may look a little different.)

Paired Conversation 2

With a partner, take turns reading the A and B parts of the conversation. Fill in each blank with the right word (or words) from the Word Bank.

WORD BANK

computer	type	WordPad	Start button	title bar
cursor	text	Enter key	Shift key	Backspace key

Student A	Hello. Are you learning to use the _____?
Student B	Yes, I am.
Student A	Will you show me how to _____ a letter to my sister?
Student B	Yes. First, open the _____ program.
Student A	I don't know how to do that.
Student B	Click the _____. Go to All Programs, Accessories, then choose WordPad.
Student A	Oh! I see "WordPad" on the _____!
Student B	Do you see the _____ blinking on the screen?
Student A	Yes, I do.
Student B	The computer is telling you that it is ready for you to type your _____.
Student A	Is there anything else that I should know before I start?
Student B	Yes. At the end of a paragraph, press the _____.
Student A	OK. Anything else?
Student B	When you want a capital letter, press the _____ and the letter.
Student A	Oh. That's good to know.
Student B	You can also erase a word with the _____.
Student A	Thanks so much for helping me.
Student B	I'm sure your sister will be happy to get your letter.

Vocabulary Worksheet

Fill in the blanks. Select the best answer for each sentence, using vocabulary words from the Word Bank.

WORD BANK

cursor	Shift key
Enter key	arrow keys
Delete key	Backspace key
spacebar	text

1. When you make a mistake and want to take away the letter or word that you just typed, and the cursor is at the end of the word, you can use the _____.

2. When you want to capitalize a letter, you press the _____ and the letter you want to capitalize at the same time.

3. When you want to start a new sentence on another line, you use the _____.

4. The _____ shows you where you are about to type text.

5. The words that you write or type are called _____.

6. Two ways to erase a letter or word are to use the Backspace key or the _____.

7. When you want to put a space between two words, you need to use the _____.

8. When you want your cursor to go to another place in the text without erasing, you can use the _____.

Verb Worksheet

Fill in the blanks. Select the best answer for each sentence, using vocabulary words from the Word Bank.

WORD BANK

delete	enter	type
wrap	insert (text)	

1. When you want to take away a word, you need to _____ it.

2. To _____ when typing text is to move to the next line.

3. When you want to add a word between two other words, you can

   _____ the word.

4. To _____ means to make the words automatically continue

   on the next line.

5. To _____ is to use the keyboard to write information on

   a page.

Missing Vowels and Consonants

Fill in the missing vowels in the left column and missing consonants in the right column. Remember: some are multiword terms.

1. spcbr   _____

2. txt   _____

3. ntr ky   _____

4. dlt ky   _____

5. bckspc ky   _____

6. crsr   _____

7. shft ky   _____

8. i - - e - -   _____

9. - - a -   _____

10. - - - e   _____

11. e - - e -   _____

12. - e - e - e   _____

13. a - - o - - e -   _____

Scrambled Words

Unscramble the letters to create your computer vocabulary words. Remember: some are multiword terms.

1. restin _____

2. reent _____

3. praw _____

4. reetn eyk _____

5. pety _____

6. ttxe _____

7. teeeld _____

8. rroucs _____

9. fitsh yke _____

10. worra seyk _____

11. eeedlt yke _____

12. aapsebkcc yek _____

13. bracspea _____

WordPad Word Search

Find the words listed in the Word Bank. Spaces and hyphens do not appear in the puzzle.

WORD BANK

ARROW KEYS	BACKSPACE KEY	CURSOR	DELETE	DELETE KEY
ENTER	ENTER KEY	INSERT	SHIFT KEY	SPACEBAR
TEXT	TYPE	WRAP		

```
S  S  R  E  G  G  R  O  H  C  X  F  D  P  H
Y  Y  P  E  G  J  W  B  R  Y  W  E  Y  A  D
Z  Y  E  A  T  U  N  D  N  S  L  H  E  O  N
T  D  V  K  C  N  K  N  V  E  D  V  K  O  W
W  L  L  C  W  E  E  M  T  U  F  W  E  E  Z
U  S  H  B  X  O  B  E  S  R  X  T  T  I  R
T  R  E  S  N  I  R  A  X  X  M  X  E  A  Z
U  V  J  W  L  C  Z  R  R  A  Y  E  L  K  J
Y  D  G  N  X  K  I  Y  A  E  X  T  E  R  W
Y  E  K  E  C  A  P  S  K  C  A  B  D  C  O
P  C  E  Y  P  E  N  T  E  R  K  E  Y  U  Z
G  U  B  V  K  R  F  R  P  K  W  T  M  R  Q
T  Q  O  S  C  I  H  W  D  U  G  W  M  S  X
U  Y  M  T  H  G  D  P  J  P  L  V  K  O  N
Y  T  T  S  L  L  Q  W  R  A  P  A  X  R  J
```

Crossword Puzzle

Fill in the words down and across to complete the puzzle.

ACROSS

4. This puts a space between words

7. The key that takes you to the next line when you are typing

8. The words and letters that you type

9. To put a word between two other words

10. To make words automatically go to the next line

11. To use the keyboard to write information on a page

12. This shows where you are going to type text

13. You place the cursor before a letter and press this key to erase it

DOWN

1. You press this when you want a capital letter or the top symbol on a key

2. To take away or erase

3. You place the cursor after a letter and press this key to erase it

5. These move your cursor to another place without erasing

6. Use this when you want to start text on another line

Doing More with WordPad

WORKBOOK 5.1 Fill in the Blanks

Write the correct word in each blank.

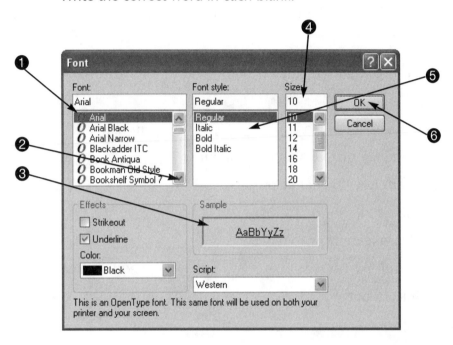

1. In the _____ _____, you choose the font name to change the font type.

2. You click on the _____ _____ to see more font types.

3. The _____ _____ box shows what the text will look like.

4. In the _____ _____, you choose a number to change text to a different size.

5. You choose regular, bold, or italic in the _____ _____ _____.

6. When you are finished, click the _____ _____.

Paired Conversation

With a partner, take turns reading the A and B parts of the conversation. Fill in each blank with the right word (or words) from the Word Bank.

WORD BANK

format	fonts	bold	italic	floppy disk
insert	floppy disk drive	print	printer	document

Student A	Today's lesson is going to be fun.
Student B	Really? Why?
Student A	We are going to learn how to _____ our text.
Student B	I heard someone say that we will learn about _____.
Student A	Yes, we will learn how to change our text.
Student B	That sounds like fun!
Student A	I know. We'll also learn how to make _____ text.
Student B	That's good, but I like the way _____ text looks better.
Student A	Well, we will learn both!
Student B	Did you bring your _____?
Student A	Yes, I did, but I don't know how to _____ it in the computer.
Student B	I'll show you how to put it in the _____.
Student A	Thanks. I don't want to mess it up.
Student B	We can put all this new stuff on our own document.
Student A	Do you think we will be able to _____ today?
Student B	I think so.
Student A	We have a nice _____ in the classroom.
Student B	Well, I'm going to be the first one to print my _____!

WORKBOOK 5.3 **Vocabulary Worksheet**

Fill in the blanks. Select the best answer for each sentence, using vocabulary words from the Word Bank.

WORD BANK

document	alignment	floppy disk
floppy disk drive	printer	font
bullets	bold print	italic print

1. The _____ is the design and size of the letters.

2. A style of lettering where the letters are thicker and darker is called

    _____.

3. _____ are special characters that you can put before items on

    a list.

4. Something written that provides information is called a _____.

5. _____ is when information is placed on one side or in the

    center.

6. A machine that puts information on a sheet of paper from the computer is

    called a _____.

7. A _____ is a narrow opening on the computer in which to

    insert the floppy disk.

8. A style of lettering where the letters are a little slanted to the right is called

    _____.

9. A plastic square that holds information that you copy from the computer is

    called a _____.

Verb Worksheet

Fill in the blanks. Select the best answer for each sentence, using vocabulary words from the Word Bank.

WORD BANK

save	decrease	highlight
insert	align	format (font)
increase	scroll	print

1. To bring text into line on one side or in the center is to

   _____ text.

2. To _____ means to keep what you did on a document in the

   computer so you can use it again later.

3. To pick the font that you want and use it in your document is to

   _____.

4. To _____ a disk is to put a disk into the floppy disk drive.

5. To make your text smaller in size is to _____ it.

6. To _____ text, you click at the beginning of a letter and drag

   the mouse to the end of what you want to change.

7. To put a document from your computer onto a sheet of paper is to

   _____.

8. To _____ means to move the contents of a window up, down,

   right, or left.

9. To _____ the text means to make the text bigger in size.

Missing Vowels

Fill in the missing vowels to complete your computer vocabulary words. Remember: some are multiword terms.

1. flppy dsk _____

2. prntr _____

3. fnt _____

4. bllts _____

5. tlc _____

6. dcmnt _____

7. bld _____

8. lgnmnt _____

9. flppy dsk drv _____

10. dcrs _____

11. lgn _____

12. scrll _____

13. hghlght _____

14. prnt _____

15. sv _____

16. frmt _____

17. nsrt _____

18. ncrs _____

Unscramble the letters to create your computer vocabulary words. Remember: some are multiword terms.

1. laciit _____

2. subletl _____

3. errtinp _____

4. ploypf kids _____

5. tomedunc _____

6. dolb _____

7. noft _____

8. ppofly kisd eirvd _____

9. talmengin _____

10. nitrp _____

11. gghhhliit _____

12. gnail _____

13. cinaeers _____

14. eavs _____

15. trofam _____

16. locslr _____

17. seeedarc _____

18. strine _____

WordPad Word Search

Find the words listed in the Word Bank. Spaces and hyphens do not appear in the puzzle.

WORD BANK

ALIGN	ALIGNMENT	BOLD	BULLETS	DECREASE	DOCUMENT
FLOPPY DISK	FLOPPY DISK DRIVE	FONT	FORMAT	HIGHLIGHT	INCREASE
INSERT	ITALIC	PRINT	PRINTER	SAVE	SCROLL

```
P  R  I  N  T  L  W  D  Y  Y  R  X  U  L  F
M  Z  L  X  D  D  B  W  E  S  P  E  M  L  M
F  N  F  M  X  O  S  H  Q  C  B  I  O  O  P
F  L  S  Z  L  U  S  K  N  U  R  P  M  R  R
K  S  I  D  Y  P  P  O  L  F  P  E  U  C  I
T  O  T  Y  S  T  V  L  R  Y  T  H  A  S  N
Q  N  F  R  A  F  E  X  D  T  H  Q  Z  S  T
A  R  E  M  E  T  K  I  A  T  G  B  Z  U  E
V  L  R  M  S  S  S  T  N  Q  I  B  V  U  R
V  O  I  R  N  K  N  E  C  I  L  A  T  I  Q
F  Y  Y  G  D  G  M  I  Z  A  H  T  X  K  E
L  K  D  R  N  U  I  G  L  A  G  Y  G  P  O
N  Z  I  D  C  Y  O  L  O  Q  I  E  V  A  S
B  V  F  O  N  T  S  U  A  V  H  H  W  I  J
E  C  D  I  N  C  R  E  A  S  E  O  H  B  S
```

Crossword Puzzle

Fill in the words down and across to complete the puzzle.

ACROSS

1. A plastic square that holds information from the computer

3. A style of lettering where the letters are heavier and darker

7. To make something bigger

8. To bring into line on one side or in the center

9. To keep what you did on the computer so you can use it again later

11. The design and size of letters

12. To put a document from your computer onto a sheet of paper

13. Something that is written and provides information

14. A narrow opening on the computer in which to insert the floppy disk

DOWN

2. To make something smaller

3. Special characters that you can put before things on a list

4. To move the contents of a window up, down, right, or left

5. A style of lettering where the letters are a little slanted to the right

6. How text is placed on one side or in the center

7. To put a disk into the floppy disk drive

10. A machine that puts information on a sheet of paper from the computer

Using the Internet

WORKBOOK 6.1 Fill in the Blanks

Write the correct word that goes in each blank.

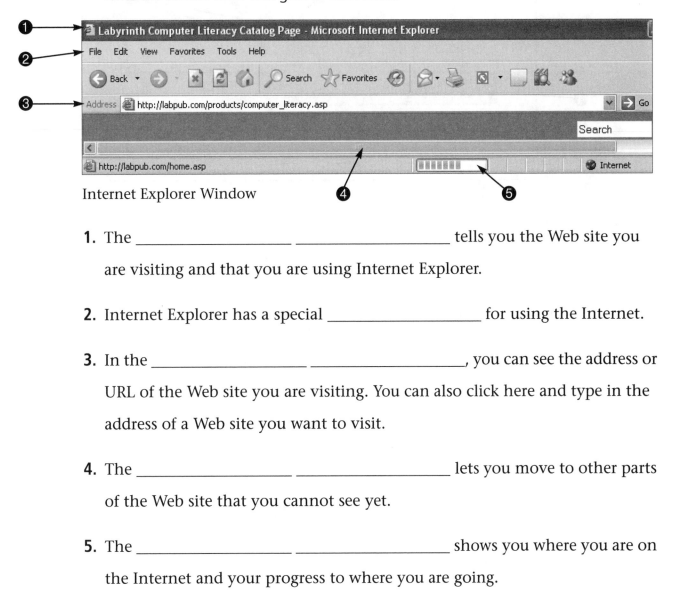

Internet Explorer Window

1. The _____ _____ tells you the Web site you are visiting and that you are using Internet Explorer.

2. Internet Explorer has a special _____ for using the Internet.

3. In the _____ _____, you can see the address or URL of the Web site you are visiting. You can also click here and type in the address of a Web site you want to visit.

4. The _____ _____ lets you move to other parts of the Web site that you cannot see yet.

5. The _____ _____ shows you where you are on the Internet and your progress to where you are going.

Write the correct word in each blank.

A Search Engine Window

1. _____

2. _____

3. _____

4. _____

Paired Conversation

With a partner, take turns reading the A and B parts of the conversation. Fill in each blank with the right word (or words) from the Word Bank.

WORD BANK

student	classroom	Internet	Web sites	search engine
Internet	visit	go	home page	connect
URL	hyperlinks	browse	simulation	search

Student A	I'm a new _____.
Student B	Welcome to our _____!
Student A	I heard that today's class is about the _____.
Student B	That's right.
Student A	Which _____ will we visit?
Student B	I'm not sure. We'll have to use a _____.
Student A	Is that what you use to look for things on the _____?
Student B	That's right.
Student A	Well, let's _____ an interesting Web site.
Student B	I know! Let's _____ to our school's _____ first.
Student A	That's a great idea. Let's _____ to it now.
Student B	Well, let's type in the _____ for our school.
Student A	OK. Now what do I do?
Student B	Well, we can use the _____ to go to the pages we want.
Student A	Thanks. Now I want to _____ the Internet.
Student B	Well, you'll have to wait. We have to do a _____ exercise first.
Student A	OK.
Student B	Later, we can _____ for other interesting subjects.

Vocabulary Worksheet

Fill in the blanks. Select the best answer for each sentence, using vocabulary words from the Word Bank.

WORD BANK

Internet	modem	hyperlink	Internet connection
scroll bar	Web site	URL	Web browser
simulation	ISP	home page	search engine

1. An object or text that takes you from one Web page to another when you click on it is called a _____.

2. A company that provides a connection to the Internet, usually for a fee, is called an _____.

3. The _____ is a system of computers from all over the world connected so they can communicate.

4. The page that opens when you open Internet Explorer is called the _____.

5. A _____ is a piece of equipment that connects your computer to the Internet.

6. Software that lets you connect to the Internet is called a _____.

7. A _____ is an exercise that is not real. It is planned ahead of time, with all the possibilities already set.

8. The place on the Internet where you can find information by using a search engine or address is called a _____.

9. An _____ is the system that connects you to the Internet.

10. A Web site you can use to look for things on the Internet is called a

_____.

11. A _____ lets you move to parts of a Web site that you

cannot yet see.

12. The unique address for each Web page is called a _____.

Verb Worksheet

Fill in the blanks. Select the best answer for each sentence, using vocabulary words from the Word Bank.

WORD BANK

browse	connect
search	visit

1. To look at an Internet Web site is to _____ it.

2. When you _____ to the Internet, you make contact with it.

3. To _____ the Internet means to look around on different Web sites.

4. To look for information on a specific topic on the Internet is called to _____.

5. I have half an hour to _____ the Internet and see if I can find a gift for my brother's birthday.

6. I am writing a book report. I will _____ the Internet for facts about my topic.

Missing Vowels and Consonants

Fill in the missing vowels of the nouns in the left column and the missing consonants of the verbs in the right column. Remember: some are multiword terms.

1. scrll br   _____

2. sp   _____

3. hm pg   _____

4. hyprlnk   _____

5. srch ngn   _____

6. smltn   _____

7. wb brwsr   _____

8. ntrnt cnnctn   _____

9. - o - e -   _____

10. U - -   _____

11. - e - - i - e   _____

12. - - o - - e   _____

13. I - - e - - e -   _____

14. - e a - - -   _____

15. - i - i -   _____

16. - o - - e - -   _____

Scrambled Words

Unscramble the letters to create your computer vocabulary words. Remember: some are multiword terms.

1. tiivs _____

2. bew sowbrer _____

3. sip _____

4. websor _____

5. reachs geenin _____

6. linekryph _____

7. mantiilous _____

8. teentrin oniennocct _____

9. mohe gape _____

10. carhes _____

11. bew itse _____

12. demom _____

13. lorscl arb _____

14. nontecc _____

15. treetnin _____

16. rul _____

Word Search

Find the words listed in the Word Bank. Spaces and hyphens do not appear in the puzzle.

WORD BANK

BROWSE	CONNECT	HOME PAGE	HYPERLINK	INTERNET
ISP	MODEM	SCROLL BAR	SEARCH	SEARCH ENGINE
SIMULATION	URL	VISIT	WEB BROWSER	WEB SITE

Crossword Puzzle

Fill in the words down and across to complete the puzzle.

ACROSS

3. The page that appears when you open Internet Explorer

6. Software that lets you connect to the Internet

7. A company that gives you a connection to the Internet

8. The unique address for each Web page

10. To look around on the Internet

14. The system lets you make contact with the Internet

15. To look at an Internet Web site

16. To look for information on a specific topic on the Internet

DOWN

1. A piece of equipment that connects your computer to the Internet

2. The place on the Internet where you can find information

4. A Web site you can use to look for things on the Internet

5. An exercise that is planned ahead of time, with all the possibilities already set

9. To make contact with the Internet

11. An object or text that takes you from one Web page to another when you click on it

12. The device that lets you move to other parts of a Web site

13. Computers from all over the world connected so they can communicate

Working with Email

WORKBOOK 7.1 **Fill in the Blanks**

Write the correct word or words in each blank.

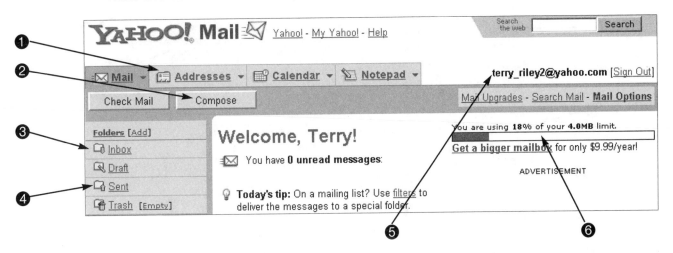

WORD BANK

Inbox	Compose	Your email address
This shows how much of your email box is being used	Addresses	Sent

1. _____ – Clicking here takes you to your address book, where you enter and keep addresses of people you want to send emails to.

2. _____ – You click here to start writing a new message.

3. _____ – A box that holds the mail sent to you. You click to open it.

4. _____ – A box that holds email that you have sent. Click to open it.

5. _____ _____ _____

6. _____

WORKBOOK 7.2 Fill in the Blanks

Write the correct words in each blank.

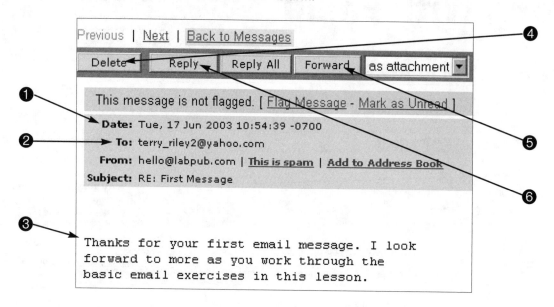

WORD BANK

The email message	Click if you want to answer the message	Your email address
Click to send the message to someone else	Date and time message was sent	Click to delete the message

1. _____

2. _____

3. _____

4. _____

5. _____

6. _____

WORKBOOK 7.3 Paired Conversation

With a partner, take turns reading the A and B parts of the conversation. Fill in each blank with the right word (or words) from the Word Bank.

WORD BANK

message	email	send	reply	compose
Webmail	username	"at"	password	Inbox

Student A	Hi. What are you doing?
Student B	I'm writing a _____ to my friend in India.
Student A	Really? How will you send it?
Student B	I'll send it to him by _____.
Student A	Is it easy to _____ an email all the way to India?
Student B	Sure it is. It's easy to _____ too.
Student A	I want to _____ and send a message, but I don't have email.
Student B	Well, you can get a _____ account.
Student A	How much does it cost?
Student B	Sometimes Webmail is free.
Student A	Really? Will you help me?
Student B	Sure. You need to choose the name you want to use.
Student A	Is that what a _____ is?
Student B	Yes. You type your username and the _____ symbol.
Student A	Do I also need a _____?
Student B	Yes, you do.
Student A	OK. Now please tell me what an Inbox is.
Student B	My _____ is on the screen now. I'll teach you how to read it.

Vocabulary Worksheet

Fill in the blanks. Select the best answer for each sentence, using vocabulary words from the Word Bank.

WORD BANK

message	button	email	password
Inbox	username	Webmail	"at" symbol

1. The character that is included in email addresses between the username and the provider name is called the _____.

2. _____ means electronic mail. It is a way to send information from one computer to another.

3. The name that you choose for your personal email account is called your _____.

4. A _____ is a personal word or combination of letters and numbers that allows you access to your email.

5. Information that you type and send to another person using email is called a _____.

6. _____ is an email service that allows you to reach your email account from computers other than your own.

7. A page in your email that lists all the messages that you have received is the _____.

8. A small rectangle that completes an action when you click it is called a _____.

Verb Worksheet

Fill in the blanks. Select the best answer for each sentence, using vocabulary words from the Word Bank.

WORD BANK

compose	send	forward	reply

1. To receive a message and then send it on to another person is to

   _____ the message.

2. To _____ a message means to transmit it from your email to

   another person's email.

3. To _____ a message means to write a message.

4. To answer a message that you received is to _____ to it.

5. I want to let my piano teacher know how much she has helped me, so I will

   _____ a nice message to show my appreciation.

6. I received a message from my cousin asking about our airline tickets to

   Hawaii. I need to _____ and let her know that I already

   bought the tickets.

7. Tomorrow is Mary's birthday. I will _____ her a message and

   wish her a happy birthday.

8. I got a very funny email message today. Do you want me to

   _____ it to you so you can read it?

Missing Vowels and Consonants

Fill in the missing vowels in the left column and the missing consonants in the right column to complete the computer vocabulary words. Remember: some are multiword terms.

1. t symbl _____

2. psswrd _____

3. wb ml _____

4. ml _____

5. sr nm _____

6. nbx _____

7. - o - - o - e _____

8. - e - - - _____

9. - o - - a - - _____

10. - e - - _____

11. - u - - o - _____

12. - e - - a - e _____

Scrambled Words

Unscramble the letters to create computer vocabulary words. Remember: some are multiword terms.

1. dorrfaw _____

2. laemi _____

3. ruse amen _____

4. plery _____

5. soopemc _____

6. nottub _____

7. bewlami _____

8. drawssop _____

9. geemass _____

10. ta lysomb _____

11. dens _____

12. nioxb _____

Word Search

Find the words listed in the Word Bank. Spaces and hyphens do not appear in the puzzle.

WORD BANK

AT SYMBOL	BUTTONS	COMPOSE	EMAIL
FORWARD	INBOX	MESSAGE	PASSWORD
REPLY	SEND	USERNAME	WEBMAIL

```
F  T  S  Y  A  N  C  F  Y  I  M  Q  O  W  K
B  A  A  W  N  O  W  L  Y  B  I  N  W  E  O
C  U  N  N  M  B  P  M  A  F  J  N  H  B  M
U  W  T  P  D  E  U  V  Q  B  A  T  B  M  L
J  I  O  T  R  R  L  V  A  E  L  W  L  A  Q
G  S  Z  R  O  L  O  I  H  N  B  O  R  I  D
E  S  E  N  D  N  Z  W  A  B  B  L  M  L  C
M  D  P  D  E  E  S  U  S  M  W  E  X  Q  Q
F  G  J  H  M  Y  C  B  Y  S  E  W  L  X  T
O  J  X  R  A  E  M  S  E  T  A  Q  B  T  J
G  H  O  F  N  W  T  J  I  A  Q  P  I  N  J
F  K  B  L  R  A  M  E  S  S  A  G  E  N  F
Y  H  N  Z  E  D  R  A  W  R  O  F  G  W  N
H  L  I  L  S  X  L  M  A  I  O  X  O  P  P
R  T  R  M  U  W  Z  X  K  R  C  X  J  U  T
```

Crossword Puzzle

Fill in the words down and across to complete the puzzle.

ACROSS

1. The character that is included in email addresses between the username and the provider name

6. The name you choose for your personal email account

8. A page in your email that lists all the messages you have received

9. To transmit a message from your email to another person's email

10. To write a message

DOWN

2. A small rectangle that completes an action when you click it

3. An email service that allows you to reach your email account from computers other than your own

4. A personal word or combination of letters and numbers that allows you access to your email

5. To send a message that you received on to another person

7. Information that you type and send to another person using email

Writing Letters in Microsoft Word

WORKBOOK 8.1 Fill in the Blanks

Write the correct word in each blank.

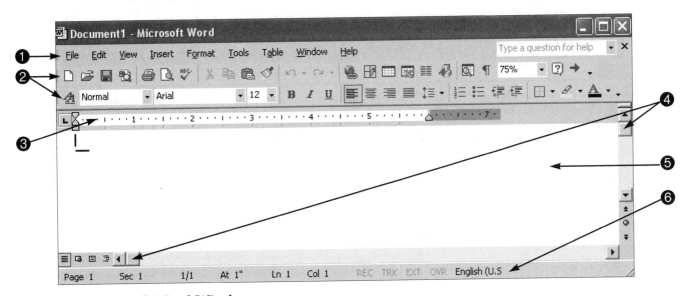

The Microsoft Word Window

1. _____

2. _____

3. _____

4. _____

5. _____

6. _____

Write the correct word in each blank.

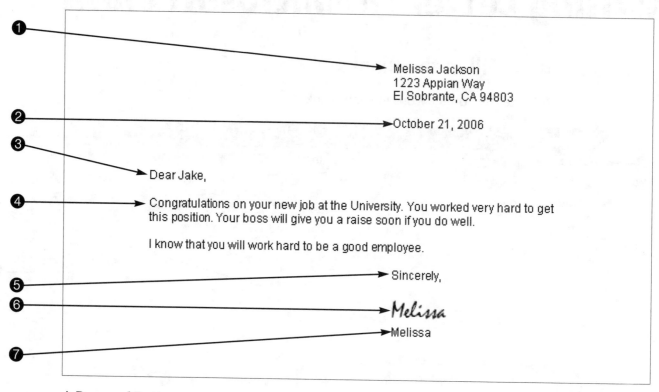

A Personal Letter

1. _____

2. _____

3. _____

4. _____

5. _____

6. _____

7. _____

Paired Conversation

With a partner, take turns reading the A and B parts of the conversation. Fill in each blank with the right word (or words) from the Word Bank.

WORD BANK

composing	greeting	business letter	format	font
Formatting	toolbar	ScreenTips	closing	spell check

Student A	Hi! What's the matter?
Student B	I'm having trouble _____ a letter to my grandma.
Student A	Why are you having trouble?
Student B	Well, I can't think of a good _____.
Student A	How about "My Dearest Grandma"?
Student B	That sounds good!
Student A	Well, you don't want it to sound like a _____!
Student B	That's true!
Student A	You should _____ your letter so it will look nice.
Student B	I know. I want a nice _____.
Student A	You also need to use your _____ toolbar.
Student B	I only know a little bit about that _____.
Student A	You should also read the _____ when they appear.
Student B	Yes, they help me a lot.
Student A	Have you thought about a _____?
Student B	I think I will write "Your Loving Granddaughter".
Student A	That sounds great. Don't forget to _____ it!
Student B	I won't!

Vocabulary Worksheet

Fill in the blanks. Select the best answer for each sentence, using vocabulary words from the Word Bank.

WORD BANK

Print Preview	ruler	Spelling and Grammar button	ScreenTip
greeting	salutation	closing	complimentary close

1. The opening words for a personal letter are called the _____.

2. The last words before you sign a business letter are called the _____.

3. _____ is a screen that lets you look at your document to see how it will look when you print it.

4. _____ is a box with information about an icon that appears when you put your mouse (without clicking) over the icon.

5. You use the _____ when you want to measure a document in your program using inches.

6. A button that you can use to check your spelling and grammar in a typed document is called the _____.

7. The last words before you sign a personal letter are called the _____.

8. The _____ refers to the opening words for a business letter.

Verb Worksheet

Fill in the blanks. Select the best answer for each sentence, using the computer verbs from the Word Bank.

WORD BANK

open	set	ignore
insert	format	spell check

1. To _____ means to pay no attention to something.

2. To _____ means to make design choices about the way your document looks.

3. To mark a point on the ruler where you want your typed words to start is called to _____ a tab.

4. To put letters or words into text that is already written is to _____ the letters or words.

5. When you _____ a document, you put a saved document on the screen.

6. When you _____, you check a document for spelling and grammar mistakes.

Missing Vowels and Consonants

Fill in the missing vowels on the left side and the missing consonants on the right side to complete the computer dictionary terms. Remember: some are multiword terms.

1. spllng nd
   grmmr bttn _____

2. pn _____

3. slttn _____

4. cmplmntry cls _____

5. spll chck _____

6. prnt prvw _____

7. ScrnTp _____

8. - - o - i - - _____

9. - o - - a - _____

10. - g - o - e _____

11. - - e e - i - - _____

12. - e - _____

13. - u - e - _____

14. i - - e - - _____

Scrambled Words

Unscramble the letters to create your computer words. Remember: some are multiword terms.

1. enersc ipt   _____

2. lintaatous   _____

3. ellps hecck   _____

4. irommtencplay   _____

    seloc   _____

5. trines   _____

6. mortaf   _____

7. neggtire   _____

8. tripn vepwire   _____

9. pone   _____

10. ringoe   _____

11. lurre   _____

12. est   _____

13. scoilgn   _____

14. pellsgin dan   _____

     mamarrg tonbut   _____

WORKBOOK 8.8 Word Search

Find the words listed in the Word Bank. Spaces and hyphens do not appear in the puzzle.

WORD BANK

CLOSING	FORMAT	GREETING
IGNORE	INSERT	OPEN
PRINT PREVIEW	RULER	SALUTATION
SCREENTIP	SET	SPELL CHECK

```
W   S   H   A   F   O   R   Z   C   C   N   G   T   T   V
E   W   C   S   B   E   R   L   J   O   K   R   R   W   Y
I   U   P   R   L   D   O   S   I   V   V   E   E   A   Y
V   G   E   U   E   S   D   T   F   F   G   E   S   X   Y
E   H   R   R   I   E   A   O   P   E   N   T   N   E   L
R   H   A   N   O   T   N   R   Y   L   B   I   I   E   T
P   P   G   W   U   N   R   T   X   A   H   N   T   Y   G
T   U   B   L   Y   B   G   H   I   Z   J   G   N   A   S
N   L   A   M   P   P   C   I   T   P   B   O   I   D   H
I   S   C   L   Y   P   F   D   S   S   X   L   E   U   O
R   T   J   Z   Z   S   E   Y   H   Q   A   R   J   U   V
P   W   J   L   D   C   N   Q   Q   N   K   R   Y   W   Z
G   I   L   K   W   S   P   E   L   L   C   H   E   C   K
D   O   U   A   D   E   D   I   G   X   Y   H   N   Y   O
Q   H   P   B   W   P   T   A   M   R   O   F   Y   K   Y
```

Crossword Puzzle

Fill in the words down and across to complete the puzzle.

ACROSS

2. A little box with information that appears when you put your mouse on an icon

4. The opening words for a personal letter

7. A tool that lets you look at your document before you print it

8. To make design choices about a document

DOWN

1. The last words before you sign a business letter

3. A way to measure a document using inches

5. To put into

6. To put a saved document on the screen

Copying and Pasting

WORKBOOK 9.1 Fill in the Blanks

Write the correct word in each blank.

The Microsoft Word toolbar and a mouse

1. _____

2. _____

3. _____

4. _____

5. _____

6. _____

7. _____

Paired Conversation

With a partner, take turns reading the A and B parts of the conversation. Fill in each blank with the right word (or words) from the Word Bank.

WORD BANK

Greetings	lesson	files	multitask	multitasking
clipboard	paste	cut	move	copy
toolbar	right-click	location	File Name box	results

Student A	_____, my friend!
Student B	Hi! Are you ready for our computer _____ today?
Student A	Yes. I have so many _____ that I need to work on.
Student B	That's great. We can _____ today.
Student A	What's _____?
Student B	It means working with two or more programs at the same time.
Student A	Oh. That's a good word.
Student B	I will teach you to copy something and put it on the _____.
Student A	And then I _____ the information somewhere else, right?
Student B	That's right. I'll also teach you how to _____ text and move it.
Student A	I really need to learn how to cut and _____ text!
Student B	Cut, _____, and paste are all on the toolbar.
Student A	Is that the _____ under the menu bar?
Student B	Right! You will also learn how to use _____ on the mouse.
Student A	Great. I know the _____ of the files I want to work on.
Student B	Good. When you finish, type the new file name in the _____.
Student A	And I'll remember where I save it.
Student B	You're doing great. The _____ will be wonderful!

Vocabulary Worksheet

Fill in the blanks. Select the best answer for each sentence, using vocabulary words from the Word Bank.

WORD BANK

Save In box	File Name box	file	Clipboard
toolbar	location	result	

1. A box that appears when you want to save a document that lets you type the name of your document is called the _____.

2. A _____ is the place where something is.

3. A _____ is a piece of work such as a letter or picture that is saved in the computer.

4. When you copy something, it goes in the _____ before you paste it in a new location.

5. The _____ is the effect of a change you make.

6. A bar with buttons that let you give commands is called a _____.

7. When you want to save a document, you will see the _____ appear to let you decide where to save your document.

Verb Worksheet

Fill in the blanks. Select the best answer for each sentence, using the computer verbs from the Word Bank.

WORD BANK

cut	copy	paste	move
undo	multitask	right-click	

1. To _____ means to change the location of text or other information.

2. To use more than one program at the same time is to _____.

3. When you _____, you take away or delete text or information that you do not want.

4. To cancel the last thing that you did is called to _____.

5. To _____ means to duplicate text in a document so you can put it in a different location.

6. To _____ means to press and release the right mouse button.

7. To _____ means to take text that you copied and put it in a different place.

Missing Vowels and Consonants

Fill in the missing vowels on the left side and the missing consonants on the right side to complete the computer dictionary terms. Remember: some are multiword terms.

1. rslt _____

2. Fl Nm bx _____

3. pst _____

4. mlttsk _____

5. Sv n bx _____

6. rght-clck _____

7. tlbr _____

8. - - i - - o a - - _____

9. - o - - _____

10. u - - o _____

11. - i - e - _____

12. - u - _____

13. - o - e - _____

14. - o - a - i o - _____

Scrambled Words

Unscramble the letters to create your computer words. Remember: some are multiword terms.

1. coolatin _____

2. uct _____

3. vaes ni oxb _____

4. taesp _____

5. doun _____

6. brootal _____

7. unigilttmask _____

8. life mane xob _____

9. robalcdip _____

10. vemo _____

11. pyco _____

12. selif _____

13. trules _____

14. gihrt kilcc _____

Word Search

Find the words listed in the Word Bank. Spaces and hyphens do not appear in the puzzle.

WORD BANK

CLIPBOARD	COPY	CUT	FILE NAME BOX
FILES	LOCATION	MOVE	MULTITASKING
PASTE	RESULT	RIGHT CLICK	SAVE IN BOX
TOOLBAR	UNDO		

```
S  X  Y  U  N  L  T  J  Y  W  F  D  M  F  E
R  T  O  T  P  Y  U  V  D  I  H  R  U  T  B
N  F  A  B  Y  Q  C  D  L  I  Q  A  L  L  I
H  M  I  N  N  X  F  E  E  N  Z  O  T  S  S
V  K  L  L  D  I  N  V  A  O  A  B  I  B  S
E  V  O  M  E  A  E  O  A  H  O  P  T  N  W
T  J  D  C  M  S  R  V  G  A  J  I  A  Q  M
U  C  O  E  P  H  I  D  A  A  Q  L  S  X  N
L  P  B  R  E  S  U  L  T  S  O  C  K  O  P
Y  O  W  R  I  W  X  Y  S  O  M  D  I  R  A
X  X  J  G  T  U  L  Y  B  A  O  T  N  O  S
K  C  I  L  C  T  H  G  I  R  A  L  G  U  T
M  D  C  A  K  S  P  U  L  C  W  R  B  J  E
P  V  L  D  I  S  X  W  O  Z  T  C  K  A  J
R  F  U  A  J  K  N  L  C  Q  M  Z  Z  A  R
```

Fill in the words down and across to complete the puzzle.

ACROSS

4. When you are using more than one program at the same time

6. To change the location of text or other information

9. To duplicate text in a document so you can put it in a different location

11. The place where something is

12. To take away or delete text or information that you do not want

13. A bar in Microsoft Word with buttons that let you give commands

DOWN

1. The effect of a change you make

2. To press and release the right mouse button

3. A box that appears when you want to save a document that lets you name your document

5. The place in the computer's memory where something goes when you copy it

7. A box that allows you to choose where to save a document

8. To cancel the last thing you did

10. To take text that you copied and put it in a new location